THE STORY OF MICHAEL JACKSON

BY TERRY COLLINS

ILLUSTRATED BY MICHAEL BYERS

Content Consultant:
Meredith E. Rutledge, Assistant Curator
Rock and Roll Hall of Fame and Museum
Cleveland, Ohio

CAPSTONE PRESS
a capstone imprint

Graphic Library is published by Capstone Press,

1710 Roe Crest Drive
North Mankato, MN 56003

www.capstonepub.com

Library of Congress Cataloging-in-Publication Data

Collins, Terry (Terry Carlson)
    King of pop : the story of Michael Jackson/
    by Terry Collins.
    p. cm. — (Graphic library. American graphic)
    Includes bibliographical references and index.
    Summary: "Describes important moments and accomplishments in Michael Jackson's life in graphic novel format"—Provided by publisher.
    ISBN 978-1-4296-6015-0 (library binding)
    ISBN 978-1-4296-7994-7 (paperback)
    ISBN 978-1-4296-9207-6 (paperback)
    1. Jackson, Michael, 1958–2009—Juvenile literature. 2. Rock musicians—United States—Biography—Juvenile literature. 3. Jackson, Michael, 1958–2009—Comic books, strips, etc. 4. Rock musicians—United States—Biography—Comic books, strips, etc. I. Title.
ML3930.J25C65 2012
782.42166092—dc23 [B]   2011034673

Printed in the United States of America in
Stevens Point, Wisconsin.
112011   006461

Direct quotations appear in orange on the following pages:

Pages 7, 10, 11, 13, 17, 18, 19, 23, from *Michael Jackson: The Magic, the Madness, the Whole Story, 1958–2009* by J. Randy Taraborrelli (New York: Grand Central Publishing, 2009).

Page 14, from "Michael Jackson's Life & Legacy: Global Superstar (1982-86)." VH1

Page 26, from *People* magazine online. Tuesday, July 07, 2009.

Photo Credit
Corbis: Bettmann, 28

Artistic Effect
Shutterstock: kaspri (vivyl record)

Art Director: Nathan Gassman

Editor: Mandy Robbins

Production Specialist: Laura Manthe

I started touring with my brothers as the Jackson 5 when I was just a little kid.

We started out in small clubs. By August 1967, we were playing at the Apollo Theater in Harlem. I was only 9 years old.

The Apollo was the toughest place of all to play. If they liked you there, they *really* liked you.

If they hated you, they'd throw food and stuff.

But you know what? We weren't scared. We knew we were good.

But surprisingly, when my brothers picked on me about *The Wiz*, Joseph stuck up for me.

You don't criticize your brother. At least he tried. How many movies have you made, big shot?

Flop or not, while working on the movie I was free. I was ready to start making my own decisions without answering to someone else.

I wanted control of my music.

Chapter 3

DON'T STOP 'TIL YOU GET ENOUGH

I met Quincy Jones while recording songs for *The Wiz*. He was the perfect music producer for me.

I don't know what it's going to sound like, but I don't want to make another Jacksons album.

We'll figure out what you need.

I'm doing this on my own. You're just going to have to understand.

My brothers were hurt that I didn't want their help, but this record was something I had to do alone.

I wrote my own songs and held nothing back. The result was four top ten singles and my first Grammy award.

MICHAEL JACKSON OFF THE WALL

Off The Wall was a hit, but I knew I could do better.

I was 21 years old. Going out on my own, away from my family, was painful, but necessary. I knew I could get farther that way.

Music has always brought our family together. We're the Jacksons. How can you abandon your brothers like this?

I'm a grown-up now, Joseph. I'm Michael Jackson. I make my own decisions.

Still, for all of my solo success, I had obligations to my brothers. We went on a final concert tour as a group in 1981, and then I was done.

Michael, what frustrates you about going on tour?

A tour takes so much time and work, and when it is over, there's nothing to show for it.

With film, you capture it, it's shown all over the world, and it's there forever.

13

When I perform, I feel like I'm giving a whole lot but for nothing. I like to capture things and hold them and share them with the world.

We're filming every rehearsal, Michael. None of the work we've done so far will ever be lost.

That's good to know, Kenny. Thank you.

Should we run the "Thriller" number next?

Absolutely. I can't wait to see the costumes!

Released on November 30, 1982, *Thriller* became the best-selling album of all time.

The title track, "Thriller," was turned into an epic 14-minute rock video.

Song after song entered the top ten charts:

"Beat It"

"Human Nature"

"The Girl Is Mine"

"PYT (Pretty Young Thing)"

"Wanna Be Startin' Something"

"Billie Jean"

... like at the taping of the *Motown 25: Yesterday, Today, and Forever* television special back in 1983.

Fantastic! That number has really come together nicely.

I think it will be a showstopper.

I love it when an audience gets caught up in a performance ...

I performed some of The Jackson 5 hits with my brothers. When we were done, they left. I found myself onstage alone.

People always told me ...

be careful what you do ...

Don't go around breaking young girls' hearts ...

But fame is a fickle monster. It brings both positive and negative attention.

From the 1980s on, tabloid newspapers and television shows picked apart the private life of Michael Jackson.

Everything Michael did was news ...

... from the transformation of his estate, Neverland Ranch, into a private amusement park and petting zoo ...

... to his appearing in the 3-D film *Captain EO*, which was shown exclusively in Disney theme parks ...

... to his new "tough guy" image for the 1987 album *Bad*.

However, even the tabloid newspapers were surprised when Michael married the daughter of Elvis Presley in 1994.

Two years later, his marriage to Lisa Marie Presley ended.

Michael's second marriage was to Debbie Rowe. She had his first son, Prince Michael, in 1997. A daughter, Paris, followed in 1998.

I have been blessed beyond comprehension, and I will work tirelessly at being the best father I can be.

Michael's second marriage ended in 1999. An unknown surrogate mother gave Michael his second son, Prince Michael II, in 2002.

BLOOD ON THE DANCE FLOOR

**The Staples Center Auditorium
June 24, 2009   11:50 p.m.**

Great job tonight, Michael!

Thank you. I think it's all coming together perfectly.

Around midnight, after several hours of rehearsal, Michael Jackson said his goodnights before leaving the Staples Center.

Those who were with him remember his excitement about the upcoming tour.

Michael reviewed some of the video footage, thanked his crew, and headed home.

Michael arrived at his rented mansion late at night. But the weary celebrity still took time to say hello to a group of fans that had gathered outside the gate.

We love you, Michael!

I love all of you too.

Suffering from chronic insomnia, an exhausted Michael struggled to sleep.

The long night was restless and led into the dawn. Once he finally fell asleep, the King of Pop never awakened.

Michael Jackson died on Thursday, June 25, 2009.

Upon news of his death, the world mourned.

Who can measure the impact of one man's life upon the world?

A shrine made by Michael's fans at his boyhood home in Gary, Indiana

Always In Our Hearts

Jackson's memorial service, July 7, 2009

WE WILL MISS YOU MICHAEL

MJ 4 EVER

Will he be best remembered for his singing? His dancing? His music videos? His charity work?

Considering his problems with his father, Joseph, maybe Michael would want to be remembered as a loving father.

Michael Jackson was many things to many people.

He was an artist, a dreamer, a father, a brother ... and an inspiration.

I just want to say that ever since I was born, Daddy has been the best father you could ever imagine ...

... and I just want to say that I love him so much.

And in his heart, he was still a little boy who never grew up ...

... and the world is all the richer for it.

On June 25, 2009, the world lost a musical icon. No list of legendary musicians would be complete without the name Michael Jackson.

The Legacy of Michael

Michael Joseph Jackson was born in Gary, Indiana on August 29, 1958. He was the eighth of 10 children. Michael's father, Joseph Jackson, saw the musical talent in his children, and served as their manager. He was very strict and made them rehearse long hours, which often upset young Michael. But the hard work paid off. By 1968 the Jackson 5 signed a contract with Motown Records. Michael took the lead role in the group, guiding them to several number one records.

As Michael matured, he wanted to record music as a solo act. In 1979 he began managing his own career. Michael was not content to limit himself to one style of performing. He led the way as an artist with crossover appeal. His songs sold to all kinds of audiences, from fans of soul to rock to easy listening. Today, Michael is credited with inventing the category of "popular" music, hence his nickname, the King of Pop.

Unfortunately, along with the triumphs came heartbreak. Michael suffered from a fireworks accident in 1984 while filming a commercial. The accident resulted in second degree burns to his scalp. Corrective plastic surgery was needed to hide the scars. This was the first of many operations Michael underwent to change his appearance.

Michael was also a pioneer in making music into a theatrical performance. He was one of the first artists to create music videos. In 1982, with the release of his album *Thriller*, he became one of the best-selling recording artists of all time. Michael's videos combined his songs with striking images. These dynamic mini-movies showcased his trend-setting dance moves and one-of-a-kind fashion sense. His video performances were seen across the globe, making him a true international superstar. His dance moves and creative theatrical innovations continue to inspire today's artists.

Two short-lived marriages, the first of them to the daughter of rock legend Elvis Presley, ended in divorce. His odd behavior and colorful image sometimes overshadowed his music. In tabloid newspapers, Michael became known as "Wacko Jacko" for his eccentric lifestyle.

For several years, Michael stayed out of the public eye. He devoted himself to raising his kids and being the kind of father he had wanted as a child. However, approaching the age of 50, Michael decided to embark on a comeback tour. His unexpected death on June 25, 2009, shocked the world. An estimated one billion people around the world watched his televised memorial service.

album (AL-buhm)—a collection of music recorded on a CD, tape, or record

chronic (KRON-ik)—describes a problem that does not get better for a long time

critic (KRI-tik)—someone who reviews art, books, or movies

eccentric (ek-SEN-trik)—acting odd or strange, but in a harmless or charming way

fickle (FIK-uhl)—someone who is fickle changes his or her mind often

induct (in-DUHKT)—to formally admit someone into a position or place of honor

innovation (in-uh-VAY-shuhn)—a new idea or invention

insomnia (in-SOM-nee-uh)—not being able to fall asleep or stay asleep

mansion (MAN-shuhn)—a large and expensive house

mourn (MORN)—to be very sad and miss someone who has died

musical (MYOO-zuh-kuhl)—a show with singing and dancing

surrogate (SUR-uh-get)—a woman who carries a baby to term for another person to raise

tabloid (TAB-loid)—a newspaper that contains brief stories and pictures that are meant to stir up interest or cause excitement

READ MORE

Collins, Terry. *Elvis: A Graphic Novel.* American Graphic. Mankato, Minn.: Capstone Press, 2011.

Gunderson, Jessica. *Jay-Z: Hip-Hop Icon.* American Graphic. Mankato, Minn.: Capstone Press, 2012.

Krohn, Katherine. *Michael Jackson: Ultimate Music Legend.* Gateway Biographies. Minneapolis: Lerner, 2010.

INTERNET

FactHound offers a safe, fun way to find Internet sites related to this book. All of the sites on FactHound have been researched by our staff.

Here's all you do:

Visit *www.facthound.com*

Type in this code: 9781429660150

Super-cool stuff! Check out projects, games and lots more at
www.capstonekids.com

AMERICAN 🇺🇸 GRAPHIC